Firsts and Seconds

AN INTRODUCTION
TO TWO-PART SINGING

William Appleby
and
Frederick Fowler

OXFORD UNIVERSITY PRESS
MUSIC DEPARTMENT WALTON STREET OXFORD OX2 6DP

LIST OF SONGS

1. Tallis's Canon
2. The Cuckoo *(traditional)*
3. All who sing, and wish to please *(T. Goodban)*
4. The hart he loves the high wood *(traditional)*
5. Now we are met *(T. Goodban)*
6. Haste thee, nymph *(Samuel Arnold)*
7. The Sandman *(German folk-tune, arr. Brahms)*
8. Blow the wind southerly *(Northumbrian folksong)*
9. The Miller's Flowers *(Schubert)*
10. Susanni *(Old German tune, arr. Fritz Jöde)*
11. The Shepherd *(Harry Brook)*
12. Song of the Spirits (from 'Armide') *(Gluck)*
13. O wha's for Scotland, and Charlie?
    (Jacobite song, arr. Herbert Horrocks)
14. Sweet Kate *(Robert Jones)*
15. Summer (from 'Alcina') *(Handel)*
16. How merrily we live *(Michael Este)*
17. The Loadstars *(William Shield)*
18. Ho-la-hi *(German folksong, arr. Roger Fiske)*
19. Song of Farewell *(Austrian folksong, arr. Ferdinand Rauter)*
20. Li'l David, play on yo' harp
    (Negro spiritual, arr. Sebastian H. Brown)
21. Cielito Lindo *(Mexican folk-tune, arr. Phyllis Tate)*

FIRSTS AND SECONDS

1. Tallis's Canon

Words by
Bishop Ken (1637-1711)

Thomas Tallis
(c. 1505-1585)

- migh - ty wings. Praise God, from whom all
- migh - ty wings. Praise

bless - ings flow; Praise him, all crea - tures here be - low; Praise
God, from whom all bless - ings flow; Praise him, all crea - tures

him a - bove, ye heav'n - ly host; Praise Fa - ther, Son, and
here be - low; Praise him a - bove, ye heav'n - ly host; Praise

Ho - ly Ghost. A - men.
Fa - ther, Son, and Ho - ly Ghost. A - men.

Firsts and Seconds

4

2. The Cuckoo

Words by
Jacqueline Froom

Traditional

Fairly quickly

mp

First Voice: From far a-way it ech - oes, His clear and joy-ful song: It rings a-cross the val - ley In spring the whole day long. "Cuc - koo, cuc - koo," he sings with might and

Second Voice: *mp* From far a-way it ech - oes, His clear and joy-ful

Firsts and Seconds

Firsts and Seconds

3. All who sing, and wish to please

T. Goodban
(1784-1863)

4. The hart he loves the high wood

Traditional

8

5. Now we are met

T. Goodban
(1784-1863)

Firsts and Seconds

6. Haste thee, nymph

Words by
John Milton

Samuel Arnold
(1740-1802)

★originally

Firsts and Seconds

7. The Sandman

Words by
Frances B. Wood

German folk-tune
arranged by Brahms

First Voice
1. When night her vel – vet cur – tain Has
(2.) smile to greet the Sand – man Who

Second Voice
Lah lah lah

drawn_ at close_ of day, She lights her star – ry
steals_ a – cross_ the skies, His ma – gic sack full

lah lah lah lah lah

lan – terns A – long_ the Milk – y Way. The_
la – den With dreams and lul – la – bies. The_

lah lah lah lah lah

Note: the second voice part has been added by the editors. The words are reprinted by permission.

Firsts and Seconds

Firsts and Seconds

8. Blow the wind southerly

Firsts and Seconds

told me last night there were ships in the off - ing, And
is it not sweet— to hear the breeze sing - ing, As

lah lah lah lah lah

I hur - ried down to the deep roll - ing sea. But my
light - ly it comes o'er the deep roll - ing sea? But—

lah lah lah lah lah lah

eye could not see it where - ev - er might be it, The
sweet - er and dear - er by far when 'tis bring - ing The

lah lah lah lah lah lah lah

bark that is bear - ing my lov - er to me.
bark of my true love in safe - ty to me.

lah lah lah lah

D.C. v. 2

Firsts and Seconds

9. The Miller's Flowers

Translated by
Arthur Langford

Franz Schubert
(1797-1828)

1. A - long the brook grow ma - ny flowers Be - low the mill in sun and showers; And past them flows the
2. Some seed - lings from the wa - ter's edge I'll plant a - long her win - dow ledge; And when the mil - ler's
3. And when night falls and she's a - sleep, The flowers a lov - ing watch will keep; But while in gen - tle

Lah lah lah lah lah lah lah lah lah

The words are reprinted by permission

Firsts and Seconds

murm - 'ring stream Whose wa - ters in ___ the
daugh - ter fair Leans out___ to breathe_ the
sleep___ she lies, They'll nev - er close___ their

lah   lah   lah

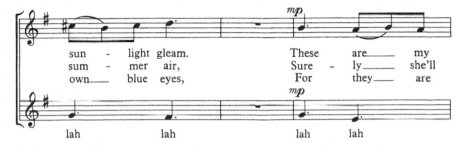

sun - light gleam. These are___ my
sum - mer air, Sure - ly___ she'll
own___ blue eyes, For they___ are

lah   lah   lah   lah

own___ for - get - me - nots, These are___ my
then___ for - get me not, Sure - ly___ she'll
my ___ for - get - me - nots, For they___ are

lah   lah   lah___   lah   lah

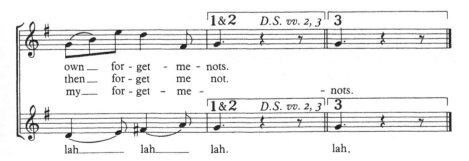

own ___ for - get - me - nots.
then___ for - get me not.
my ___ for - get - me - - nots.

lah___   lah___   lah.   lah.

Firsts and Seconds

10. Susanni

Carol in two parts

15th-century words

Old German tune
arranged by Fritz Jöde

A lit - tle child there is___ y - born,

A

Ei - a, ei - a, su - san - ni,

lit - tle child there is___ y - born, su - san - ni,

su - san - ni, su - san - ni. And he sprang out of

su - san - ni, su - san - ni. And he sprang

Jes - se's thorn, Al - le - lu - ya___

Divisi:
Al - le - lu - -

out___ of Jes - se's thorn,___ Al - le - lu -

Firsts and Seconds

To save__ us all__ that were for - lorn.

2. Now Jesus is the childès name,
   And Mary mild she is his dame;
   And so our sorrow is turned to game.

3. It fell upon the high midnight,
   The stars they shone both fair and bright,
   The angels sang with all their might.

4. Three kings there came with their presénts
   Of myrrh and gold and frankincense,
   As clerkès sing in their sequence.

5. Now sit we down upon our knee,
   And pray we to the Trinity,
   Our help, and succour for to be.

Words from *The Oxford Book of Carols*, by permission

11. The Shepherd

Words by
William Blake

Harry Brook

Moderato semplice

First Voice: How sweet is the_ shep-herd's sweet lot!___ From the morn to the_ eve-ning he_ strays;___ He shall fol - low his sheep all_ the day,___ And his tongue shall be fill - ed_ with praise. For he

Second Voice: How sweet is the_ shep-herd's sweet lot!___ From the morn to the_ eve - ning he_ strays;___ He shall fol - low his sheep all_ the day, And his tongue shall be fill - ed_ with_ praise. For he

poco ten.

rall.   *a tempo*   *pp*

12. Song of the Spirits

from 'Armide'

Words by
Jacqueline Froom

Gluck (1714-1787)
Edited and arranged by
W. G. Whittaker

Firsts and Seconds

1. -las! from the earth ne - ver free._____
2. still our dear home - land we see._____

2. an - guish: our home - land we see._____

CHORUS *(to be sung by both voices in both verses)*
p cresc.

Life! Thou must let us go! How -

p cresc.

Life! Thou must let us go! How -

mf　　　　　　　*p*

- ev - er we re - gret, O free_ us from be -

mf　　　　　*p*

- ev - er we re - gret, O free_ us from be -

cresc.　　　　*mf*　　*cresc.*

- low: The world we_ must for - get._ Hea - ven's_

cresc.　　　*mf*　　*cresc.*

- low: The world we must for - get. Hea - ven's_

f　　　　*D.C. v. 2*

gates o - pen_ wide And we must there a - bide._

f　　　　*D.C. v. 2*

gates o - pen_ wide And we must there a - bide.

Firsts and Seconds

13. Oh, wha's for Scotland and Charlie?

Traditional (Jacobite)
arranged by Herbert Horrocks

Firsts and Seconds

wha's— for Scot - land and Char - lie?
on — for Scot - land and Char - lie. A -

wha's for Scot - land and Char - lie?
on for Scot - land and Char - lie. A -

molto animato

- wa', *a - wa', auld car - lie, a -

- wa', *a - wa', auld car - lie, a -

- wa', a - wa', auld car - lie, Gi'e —

- wa', a - wa', auld car - lie,

Char - lie his crown,— and let him sit down **Whaur

Whaur

D.S. v. 2 4

ye've been sae lang,— auld car - lie! *After second verse*

D.S. v. 2 4

ye've been sae lang, auld car - lie!

*Awa', auld carlie, = away old fellow.
**Whaur ye've been sae lang = where you've been so long.

Firsts and Seconds

14. Sweet Kate

Robert Jones (1609)

she,
Glad - ly would I
she,
Make no fool of

Glad - ly would I see
Make no fool of me!

see
A - ny man to die with_ lo - -
me!
Men I know have oaths at_ plea - -

A - ny man to die with lo - - -
Men I know have oaths at plea - - -

- ving.
mp
Nev - er a - ny
- sure.
But their hopes at -

- ving.
Nev - er a - ny yet
- sure.
mp
But their hopes at - tained,

yet
Died of such a fit,
Nei- ther have I
- tained,
They be - wray they feigned,
And their oaths are

Died of such a fit,
Nei - ther have I fear of
They be - wray they feigned,
And their oaths are kept at

D.C. v. 2

fear of_ pro - - - ving.
kept at_ lei - - - sure.

D.C. v. 2

pro - - - - - ving.
lei - - - - - sure.

Firsts and Seconds

15. Summer

(Air from 'Alcina')

Words by
Jacqueline Froom

Handel
(1685-1759)

Larghetto

First Voice: Stiff - ly stands the burn - ished bar - ley

Second Voice: Stiff - ly stands the burn - ished bar - ley

Wait - ing for the reap - er's hook, reap - er's hook.

Wait - ing for the reap - er's hook, reap - er's hook.

Hea - vy bees fly slow - ly home -ward, Slug - gish

Hea - vy bees fly slow - ly home-ward, Slug - gish

as the la - zy brook, slug - gish as the la - zy

as the la - zy brook, slug - gish as the la - zy

Firsts and Seconds

Firsts and Seconds

16. How merrily we live

Michael Este
(c. 1580–c. 1648)

Firsts and Seconds

17. The Loadstars

Words adapted
from Shakespeare

William Shield
(1748-1829)

Firsts and Seconds

shep-herd's ear. O hap-py, hap-py, hap-py, hap-py

shep-herd's ear. O hap-py, hap-py

fair,_ Your eyes are load-stars, and your tongue sweet air.

fair,_ are load-stars, and your tongue sweet air.

More tune - a -ble than lark_ to shep - herd's_ ear,

More

to shep-herd's ear, When

tune - a -ble than lark_ to shep - herd's ear,_ When

wheat is green, when haw-thorn buds ap - pear, When wheat is

wheat is green, when haw-thorn buds ap - pear, When wheat is

Firsts and Seconds

Firsts and Seconds

18. Ho-la-hi

Translated by
Roger Fiske

German folk-song
arranged by Roger Fiske

Lis-ten to the cheer-ful cry,

Ho-la-hi, ho-la-ho, Is my sweet-heart

pass-ing by? Ho-la-hi-a-ho! No, the

voice fades down the street, Ho-la-hi,

ho-la-ho, That was not my dar-ling

sweet, Ho-la-hi-a-ho.

First Voice
I-dle peo-ple ques-tion me, Ho-la-hi,

Second Voice
I-dle peo-ple ques-tion me, Ho-la-hi,

Firsts and Seconds

ho - la - ho, What my true love's name can be,

ho - la - ho, What my true love's name can be,

Ho - la - hi - a - ho. Let them won - der,

Ho - la - hi - a - ho. Let them won - der,

let them tease, Ho - la - hi, ho - la - ho,

let them tease, Ho - la - hi, ho - la - ho,

I shall love just— as I please, Ho - la - hi - a -

I shall love just— as I please, Ho - la - hi - a -

- ho.

- ho.

Spite - ful peo - ple

Firsts and Seconds

Ho - la - hi, ho - la - ho.

some - times hiss, Ho - la - hi, ho - la - ho.

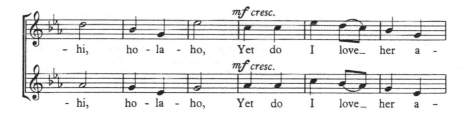

Ho - la - hi - a -

"No - thing good can come of this," Ho - la - hi - a -

- ho. "She will ne - ver__ be your own," Ho - la -

- ho. "She will ne - ver__ be your own," Ho - la -

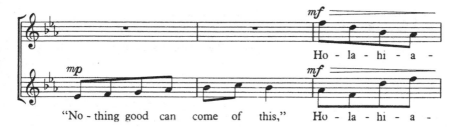

- hi, ho - la - ho, Yet do I love__ her a -

- hi, ho - la - ho, Yet do I love__ her a -

- lone, Ho - la - hi - a - ho, Ho - la - hi!

- lone, Ho - la - hi - a - ho, Ho - la - hi!

Firsts and Seconds

19. Song of farewell

Words by
Ursula Vaughan Williams

*Austrian folk-song
Collected by Engel Lund
Arranged by Ferdinand Rauter

Ⓒ Oxford University Press 1961

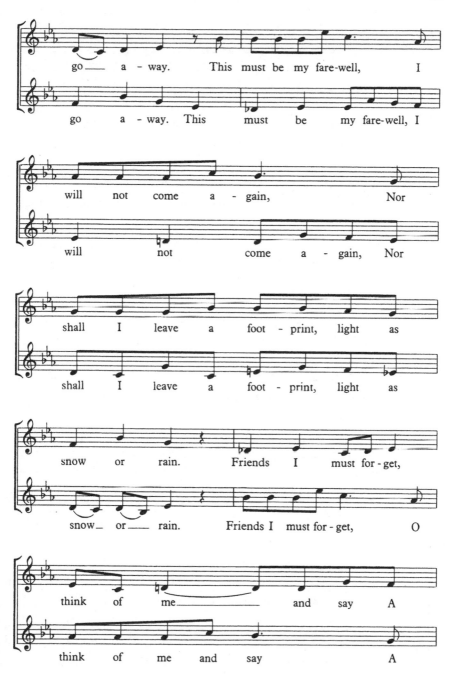

Firsts and Seconds

20. Li'l David play on yo' harp

Negro Spiritual
arranged by Sebastian H. Brown

Firsts and Seconds

42

Hal - le - lu.

play on yo' harp, Hal - le - lu.

1. Da - vid was a shep - herd boy,___ He kill Go -
2. Josh - u' was de son ob Nun,___ He ne'er would

1. Da - vid was a shep - herd boy,___ He kill Go -
2. Josh - u' was de son ob Nun,___ He ne'er would

- li'h an' shout fo' joy.___ Da - vid was a
quit till work be done. ___ Josh - u' was de

- li'h an' shout fo' joy.___
quit till work be done.___

shep - herd boy,___ He kill Go - li'h an'
son ob Nun,___ He ne'er would quit till

(Li'l Da - vid play on yo' harp), He kill an'
(Li'l Da - vid play on yo' harp), He ne'er would

Firsts and Seconds

Firsts and Seconds

21. Cielito Lindo

Words by
Jacqueline Froom

Mexican folk-tune
arranged by Phyllis Tate

★ Pronounced "See*ay*-lee-to"

Firsts and Seconds

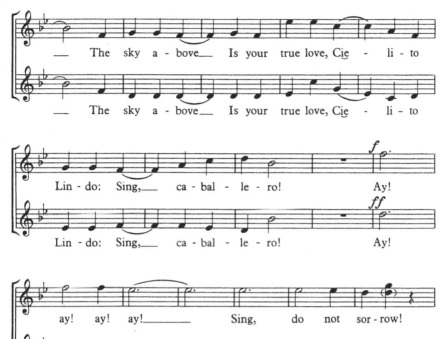

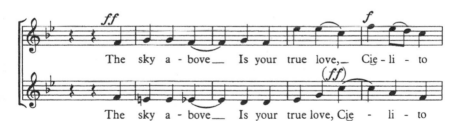

Firsts and Seconds

OXFORD UNIVERSITY PRESS